Once you have identified your target topics and created your catch... open the books and get revising. The Revision Guide and Revision W... have matching page numbers to help you find your way around quickl...

Your **Revision Guide** is packed with essential facts, key skills and worked examples to help you stay ahead of the game. Each page covers a single topic so you can stay organised, and the book covers your **whole course**, so once you're back up to speed you will be able to use it alongside your school work, and to revise for your exams.

Check that you have nailed each topic by practising some exam-style questions on the corresponding page in the **Revision Workbook**. There are **guided questions** which give you part of the working, and hints and tips to help you get started. And when the exams are a bit closer, you can use the **exam-style practice papers** to check that you are exam-ready.

Find your catch-up topics

If you know which units or topics you want to revise, you can use the **Matching chart** to find the corresponding Revision Guide and Workbook pages. Your teacher or tutor might be able to tell you which units or topics you missed, or you might recognise them from the work you did at home during lockdown.

Tick the units or topics you want to revise, then add those page numbers to your catch-up plan on page 15.

Pages 18–19

Knowledge check

You can use the diagnostic self-test on the next 11 pages to help you create your own customised catch-up plan. Each question checks a different key skill or piece of core knowledge from your GCSE course. If you feel that you need more help with that topic or skill, add the page numbers shown in the arrows to your catch-up plan.

A bit at a time

There are 70 questions in this knowledge check. Have a go at them in chunks. When you have done a batch of 10 or 20 questions, check your answers on the back cover (page 20) of this booklet. Then take a break or come back and try some more in another study session!

Number

1 Factors and primes

Express 600 as a product of its prime factors.

- [ ] **A** $2^2 \times 5^2 \times 6$
- [ ] **B** $2^3 \times 3^2 \times 5^3$
- [ ] **C** $2^3 \times 3 \times 5^2$
- [ ] **D** $2 \times 3 \times 10^2$

[✓] [X] **Revise page 1** →

2 Indices

Write $\dfrac{7^{10} \times 7^3}{7}$ as a single power of 7.

- [ ] **A** 7^{29}
- [ ] **B** 7^{12}
- [ ] **C** 7^{23}
- [ ] **D** 7^{-13}

[✓] [X] **Revise pages 2, 3** →

3 Rounding

Round 0.0473508 to 3 significant figures.

- [ ] **A** 0.047
- [ ] **B** 0.0473
- [ ] **C** 0.0474
- [ ] **D** 0.05

[✓] [X] **Revise page 4** →

4 Mixed numbers

Work out $1\frac{7}{8} \times 3\frac{2}{5}$

- [ ] **A** $6\frac{3}{8}$
- [ ] **B** $4\frac{9}{13}$
- [ ] **C** $3\frac{7}{20}$
- [ ] **D** $5\frac{1}{8}$

[✓] [X] **Revise page 5** →

5 Standard form

Write 736 000 in standard form.

- [ ] **A** 7.36×10^3
- [ ] **B** 736×10^3
- [ ] **C** 7.36×10^5
- [ ] **D** 7.36×10^{-6}

[✓] [X] **Revise page 8** →

6 Recurring decimals

Write the recurring decimal $0.0\dot{5}$ as a fraction. Do not use a calculator.

- [ ] **A** $\frac{5}{9}$
- [ ] **B** $\frac{1}{18}$
- [ ] **C** $\frac{1}{20}$
- [ ] **D** $\frac{5}{99}$

[✓] [X] **Revise pages 6, 9** →

7 Upper and lower bounds

The length of a carrot is 20 cm, rounded to the nearest cm.

What is the upper bound for this length?

☐ **A** 20.5 cm ☐ **B** 20.49 cm

☐ **C** 25 cm ☐ **D** 19.5 cm

☑ ☒ **Revise pages 10, 11** ▶

8 Surds

Write $\dfrac{3}{1-\sqrt{2}}$ in the form $a + b\sqrt{2}$,

where a and b are integers.

Do not use a calculator.

☐ **A** $3 + 3\sqrt{2}$ ☐ **B** $3 - 3\sqrt{2}$

☐ **C** $3 - \dfrac{1}{3}\sqrt{2}$ ☐ **D** $-3 - 3\sqrt{2}$

☑ ☒ **Revise pages 12, 49** ▶

9 Counting

This combination lock uses two letters from A to Z and two digits from 0 to 9.

C	X	0	5

Work out the total number of possible combinations.

☐ **A** 67 600 ☐ **B** 72

☐ **C** 6760 ☐ **D** 260

☑ ☒ **Revise page 13** ▶

Algebra

10 Algebraic indices

Simplify $(x^2y)^3$

☐ **A** x^2y^3 ☐ **B** x^5y^3

☐ **C** xy^6 ☐ **D** x^6y^3

☑ ☒ **Revise page 16** ▶

11 Expanding brackets

Expand and simplify
$3(4a + b) - 2(a - 2b)$

☐ **A** $10a - b$ ☐ **B** $10a + 7b$

☐ **C** $9a + 7b$ ☐ **D** $5a + b$

☑ ☒ **Revise page 17** ▶

12 Double bracket

Expand and simplify $(2x + 3)^2$

☐ **A** $4x^2 + 9$ ☐ **B** $2x^2 + 6x + 9$

☐ **C** $4x^2 + 12x + 9$ ☐ **D** $4x^2 + 6x + 9$

☑ ☒ **Revise page 17** ▶

13 Factorising

Factorise $x^2 - 4x - 12$

☐ **A** $4x(x - 3)$ ☐ **B** $(x - 4)(x + 3)$

☐ **C** $(x - 6)(x + 2)$ ☐ **D** $(x - 4)^2$

☑ ☒ **Revise page 18** ▶

Knowledge check

14 Linear equations

Solve $6x + 2 = 8x - 1$

- ☐ **A** $x = 0.75$
- ☐ **B** $x = 2$
- ☐ **C** $x = -1$
- ☐ **D** $x = 1.5$

☑ ☒ Revise page 19

15 Equations with fractions

Solve $\dfrac{x}{5} + \dfrac{x-1}{3} = 1$

- ☐ **A** $x = \dfrac{1}{3}$
- ☐ **B** $x = \dfrac{5}{2}$
- ☐ **C** $x = -3$ or $x = -5$
- ☐ **D** $x = 8$

☑ ☒ Revise page 20

16 Formulae

$P = 5Q^2 - 2QR$

Find the value of P when
$Q = 4$ and $R = -3$

- ☐ **A** 76
- ☐ **B** 104
- ☐ **C** 112
- ☐ **D** 56

☑ ☒ Revise page 21

17 Sequences

Find an expression for the nth term of this sequence.

8   11   14   17   20

- ☐ **A** $3n + 5$
- ☐ **B** $5n + 3$
- ☐ **C** $8n + 3$
- ☐ **D** $20 - 3n$

☑ ☒ Revise pages 22, 24

18 Straight line graphs

Find the equation of this straight line.

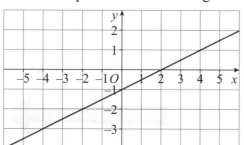

- ☐ **A** $y = 2x - 1$
- ☐ **B** $y = \dfrac{1}{2}x - 1$
- ☐ **C** $y = -x + 2$
- ☐ **D** $y = 2x + 1$

☑ ☒ Revise pages 25, 26

19 Parallel and perpendicular lines

The line **L** has equation $2x + y = 5$

Which one of the following lines is perpendicular to **L**?

- ☐ **A** $y = 2x - 5$
- ☐ **B** $y = 5 - 2x$
- ☐ **C** $y = \dfrac{1}{2}x + 10$
- ☐ **D** $y = -\dfrac{1}{2}x$

☑ ☒ Revise page 27

20 Harder graphs

Match this graph to the correct equation.

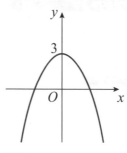

- ☐ **A** $y = 3 - x^2$
- ☐ **B** $y = x^2 - 3$
- ☐ **C** $y = x^2 + 3$
- ☐ **D** $y = x^3$

☑ ☒ Revise pages 28, 29, 43

21 Distance–time graphs

The distance–time graph shows a hike.

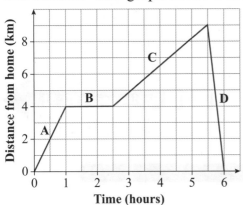

During which section was the hiker stationary?

☐ **A**   ☐ **B**   ☐ **C**   ☐ **D**

☑ ☒ Revise page 30

22 Quadratic equations

Solve the equation $x^2 - 10x + 16 = 0$

☐ **A** $x = 1.6$ ☐ **B** $x = -4$

☐ **C** $x = 8$ or $x = 2$ ☐ **D** $x = -8$ or $x = -2$

☑ ☒ Revise pages 31, 32

23 Completing the square

Write $x^2 + 6x - 1$ in the form $(x + p)^2 + q$
where p and q are integers.

☐ **A** $(x + 3)^2 - 9$ ☐ **B** $(x + 6)^2 - 37$

☐ **C** $(x + 6)^2 - 8$ ☐ **D** $(x + 3)^2 - 10$

☑ ☒ Revise page 33

24 Simultaneous equations

Solve the simultaneous equations
$5x + 6y = 5$
$x - 2y = 9$

☐ **A** $x = -3, y = 1.5$ ☐ **B** $x = 4, y = -2.5$

☐ **C** $x = 2.5, y = 5$ ☐ **D** $x = -3, y = -1.5$

☑ ☒ Revise pages 34, 35

25 Equation of a circle

What is the equation
of this circle?

☐ **A** $x^2 + y^2 = 4$

☐ **B** $x + y = 4$

☐ **C** $x + y = 16$

☐ **D** $x^2 + y^2 = 16$

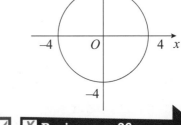

☑ ☒ Revise page 36

26 Inequalities

Solve the inequality $3x + 1 < x - 5$

☐ **A** $x > 3$ ☐ **B** $x > -3$

☐ **C** $x < -2$ ☐ **D** $x < -3$

☑ ☒ Revise pages 37, 38

27 Trigonometric graphs

How many solutions does the equation
$4 \sin x + 3 = 2$ have in the range 0° to 180°?

☐ **A** 0   ☐ **B** 1

☐ **C** 2   ☐ **D** 4

☑ ☒ Revise page 39

28 Transforming graphs

The graph with equation $y = f(x)$

is translated by vector $\begin{pmatrix} -1 \\ 5 \end{pmatrix}$

Which of the following is the equation of the
translated graph?

☐ **A** $y = -f(x) + 5$

☐ **B** $y = f(x + 1) + 5$

☐ **C** $y = f(x - 1) + 5$

☐ **D** $y = f(x - 1) - 5$

☑ ☒ Revise page 40

29 Regions on graphs

Write down the set of inequalities that defines the shaded region R.

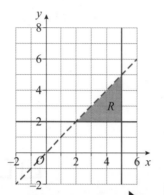

☐ **A** $x \leq 5, y \geq 2, x > y$

☐ **B** $y \geq 2, x \leq 5, x < y$

☐ **C** $y > 2, x < 5, x \leq y$

☐ **D** $y \geq 5, x \leq 2, x < y$

☑ ☒ **Revise page 41**

30 Iteration

Use the iterative formula $x_{n+1} = \sqrt{x_n^2 - 1}$ with $x_0 = 3$ to work out x_2.

Round your answer to 3 decimal places.

☐ **A** 2.65

☐ **B** 2.83

☐ **C** 2.45

☐ **D** 1.41

☑ ☒ **Revise page 45**

31 Rearranging formulae

$M = 6R - 20$

Rearrange the formula to make R the subject.

☐ **A** $R = \dfrac{M + 20}{6}$

☐ **B** $R = 6M + 20$

☐ **C** $R = \dfrac{M}{6} + 20$

☐ **D** $R = \dfrac{1}{6}(M - 20)$

☑ ☒ **Revise page 46**

32 Fractions and quadratic equations

Solve the equation $\dfrac{2}{1+x} + \dfrac{4}{x} = 5$

☐ **A** $x = 6$

☐ **B** $x = -0.8$ or $x = 1$

☐ **C** $x = -4$ or $x = 1$

☐ **D** $x = 0.8$ or $x = -1$

☑ ☒ **Revise pages 47, 48**

33 Functions

$f(x) = (2x - 3)^2$

Find $f(-1)$

☐ **A** –25

☐ **B** 1

☐ **C** –11

☐ **D** 25

☑ ☒ **Revise pages 50, 51**

34 Proof

n is an integer.

Which of the following is an even number?

☐ **A** $(n+1)(n-1)$

☐ **B** $2n-1$

☐ **C** $(n+1)^2$

☐ **D** $(n+1) + (n-1)$

☑ ☒ **Revise page 52**

35 Velocity–time graphs

The velocity–time graph shows the velocity of a runner.

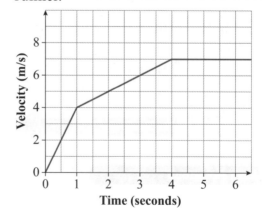

How far did the runner travel in the first 5 seconds of the race?

☐ **A** 8 m

☐ **B** 13.5 m

☐ **C** 25.5 m

☐ **D** 51 m

☑ ☒ **Revise pages 55, 56**

Ratio and proportion

36 Percentages

Work out 15% of £900

☐ **A** £145 ☐ **B** £1035

☐ **C** £135 ☐ **D** £180

☑ ☒ **Revise page 59**

37 Ratio

The ratio of juice to water in a drink is 3:2
The total amount of drink is 600 ml.

How much juice is in the drink?

☐ **A** 200 ml ☐ **B** 360 ml

☐ **C** 400 ml ☐ **D** 450 ml

☑ ☒ **Revise pages 60, 61**

38 Percentage change

In a sale, prices are reduced by 20%.
The sale price of a phone is £144.

Work out its original price.

☐ **A** £180 ☐ **B** £172.80

☐ **C** £192 ☐ **D** £115.20

☑ ☒ **Revise pages 62, 63**

39 Exponential growth

Alison invests £800 in a savings account,
which pays 2.5% compound interest.

Work out the amount Alison has in her
account after 4 years.

Give your answer to the nearest pound.

☐ **A** £883 ☐ **B** £861

☐ **C** £1953 ☐ **D** £880

☑ ☒ **Revise page 64**

40 Speed

A cyclist travels 84 km at an average
speed of 15 km/h.

Work out the total time taken.

☐ **A** 4.5 hours

☐ **B** 0.18 hours

☐ **C** 1260 hours

☐ **D** 5.6 hours

☑ ☒ **Revise page 65**

41 Compound measures

The diagram shows a solid brass cuboid.

The density of brass is 8.6 g/cm³.

Work out the mass of the cuboid.

☐ **A** 498 g ☐ **B** 27.9 g

☐ **C** 2064 g ☐ **D** 14.3 kg

☑ ☒ **Revise pages 66, 67, 82**

42 Proportionality

y is inversely proportional to x
When $x = 40$, $y = 9$.

Work out the value of x when $y = 24$.

☐ **A** 106.7 ☐ **B** 15

☐ **C** 20 ☐ **D** 12

☑ ☒ **Revise pages 68, 69, 70**

Knowledge check

Geometry and measures

43 **Angle properties**

Work out the size of the angle marked x.

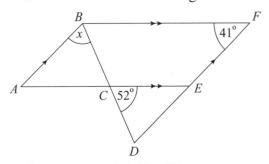

☐ **A** 52°   ☐ **B** 9°

☐ **C** 87°   ☐ **D** 93°

☑ ☒ **Revise pages 73, 74**

44 **Angles in polygons**

A is a regular octagon and **B** is a regular pentagon.

Work out the size of the angle marked x.

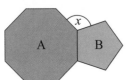

☐ **A** 117°   ☐ **B** 135°

☐ **C** 108°   ☐ **D** 243°

☑ ☒ **Revise page 75**

45 **Pythagoras' theorem**

Work out the length of BC in this right-angled triangle, correct to 1 decimal place.

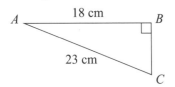

☐ **A** 5.0 cm   ☐ **B** 14.3 cm

☐ **C** 29.2 cm   ☐ **D** 205.0 cm

☑ ☒ **Revise page 76**

46 **Trigonometry**

Work out the size of the angle marked x in this right-angled triangle, to the nearest degree.

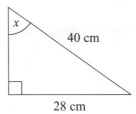

☐ **A** 55°   ☐ **B** 35°

☐ **C** 46°   ☐ **D** 44°

☑ ☒ **Revise pages 77, 79**

47 **Perimeter and area**

Work out the area of this trapezium.

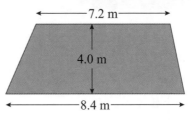

☐ **A** 33.6 m²   ☐ **B** 62.4 m²

☐ **C** 31.2 m²   ☐ **D** 37.2 m²

☑ ☒ **Revise page 80**

48 **Units of area and volume**

Convert 280 cm² into m².

☐ **A** 2.8 m²

☐ **B** 0.28 m²

☐ **C** 28 000 m²

☐ **D** 0.028 m²

☑ ☒ **Revise page 81**

49 Cylinders

Work out the volume of this cylinder, to the nearest cm³.

☐ **A** 377 cm³

☐ **B** 1131 cm³

☐ **C** 360 cm³

☐ **D** 1885 cm³

←—6 cm—→

10 cm

☑ ☒ **Revise page 83**

50 Sectors of circles

The diagram shows a circle with centre O and radius 5 cm.

Work out the area of the shaded sector to 3 significant figures.

5 cm

O 115°

☐ **A** 26.2 cm²

☐ **B** 7.98 cm²

☐ **C** 25.1 cm²

☐ **D** 627 cm²

☑ ☒ **Revise page 84**

51 3D solids

Volume of a pyramid = $\frac{1}{3}$ × base area × vertical height

A 3D solid is formed by attached a pyramid to a cube of side length 9 cm. The height of the whole solid is 20 cm.

Work out the volume of the solid.

20 cm

9 cm

☐ **A** 540 cm³

☐ **B** 1026 cm³

☐ **C** 1269 cm³

☐ **D** 1620 cm³

☑ ☒ **Revise pages 85, 87**

52 Transformations

Describe fully the single transformation that maps triangle **P** onto triangle **Q**.

☐ **A** Reflection

☐ **B** Rotation

☐ **C** Rotation 180° about (2, 2.5)

☐ **D** Reflection in the line $x = 2$

☑ ☒ **Revise pages 88, 90**

53 Bearings

The bearing of point P from point Q is 208°.

Find the bearing of point Q from point P.

☐ **A** 018°   ☐ **B** 28°

☐ **C** 028°   ☐ **D** 388°

☑ ☒ **Revise pages 91, 92**

54 Loci and constructions

Which of the following describes the points in the shaded region?

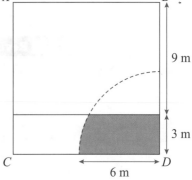

9 m

3 m

6 m

☐ **A** Closer to D than A and at least 9 m from AB

☐ **B** Less than 3 m from CD and less than 6 m from D

☐ **C** At least 9 m from AB and less than 6 m from D

☐ **D** Less than or equal to 6 m from D and less than 3 m from CD

☑ ☒ **Revise pages 93, 95**

Knowledge check

55 Congruency

Which of the following is **not** a condition of congruency for triangles?

- [ ] **A** All three angles equal
- [ ] **B** Two sides and the included angle equal
- [ ] **C** All three sides equal
- [ ] **D** Right-angle with hypotenuse and one other side equal

☑ ☒ **Revise page 96**

56 Similar shapes

The diagram shows two similar triangles.

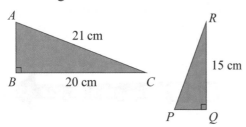

Find the length of side *PR*.

- [ ] **A** 18 cm
- [ ] **B** 14.3 cm
- [ ] **C** 20 cm
- [ ] **D** 15.75 cm

☑ ☒ **Revise pages 97, 98**

57 Triangles without right-angles

Work out the length of side *x*.

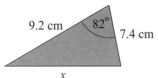

- [ ] **A** 120.5 cm
- [ ] **B** 7.5 cm
- [ ] **C** 11.0 cm
- [ ] **D** 9.1 cm

☑ ☒ **Revise pages 99, 101**

58 Lengths in 3D shapes

Work out the length of the long diagonal *AH* in this cuboid.

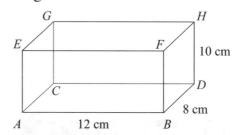

- [ ] **A** 17.5 cm
- [ ] **B** 14.4 cm
- [ ] **C** 14.8 cm
- [ ] **D** 15.9 cm

☑ ☒ **Revise pages 102, 103**

59 Circle theorems

Work out the size of angle *x*.

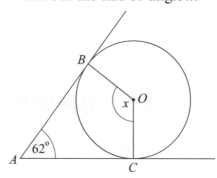

- [ ] **A** 124°
- [ ] **B** 118°
- [ ] **C** 152°
- [ ] **D** 110°

☑ ☒ **Revise pages 104, 105**

60 Vectors

$\mathbf{p} = \begin{pmatrix} -2 \\ 5 \end{pmatrix}$ and $\mathbf{q} = \begin{pmatrix} 3 \\ -3 \end{pmatrix}$

Work out the vector $\mathbf{p} - 2\mathbf{q}$

- [ ] **A** $\begin{pmatrix} 4 \\ -1 \end{pmatrix}$
- [ ] **B** $\begin{pmatrix} -1 \\ 8 \end{pmatrix}$
- [ ] **C** $\begin{pmatrix} -4 \\ 8 \end{pmatrix}$
- [ ] **D** $\begin{pmatrix} -8 \\ 11 \end{pmatrix}$

☑ ☒ **Revise pages 106, 107**

Statistics and probability

61 Averages

The table shows the number of goals scored by a team in 40 matches.

Goals	0	1	2	3	4
Frequency	11	15	8	5	1

Work out the mean number of goals scored per match.

- [ ] **A** 2 goals
- [ ] **B** 8 goals
- [ ] **C** 1.25 goals
- [ ] **D** 2.5 goals

☑ ☒ **Revise pages 110, 111**

62 Interquartile range

The stem-and-leaf diagram shows the weights of 19 satsumas.

6	4 9
7	0 1 5 5 6 9
8	2 4 7 7 7 8 8
9	0 1 3 6

Key: 6 | 4 means 64 grams

Work out the interquartile range of the weights.

- [ ] **A** 32 grams
- [ ] **B** 75 grams
- [ ] **C** 13 grams
- [ ] **D** 17 grams

☑ ☒ **Revise page 112**

63 Graphs

Describe the relationship shown on this scatter graph.

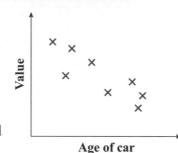

- [ ] **A** exponential decay
- [ ] **B** positive correlation
- [ ] **C** direct proportion
- [ ] **D** negative correlation

☑ ☒ **Revise pages 113, 114**

64 Collecting data

Which of the following **does not** describe a random sample.

- [ ] **A** Writing names in alphabetical order and choosing the first ten names
- [ ] **B** Assigning a number to each person and using a random number generator
- [ ] **C** Choosing names out of a hat
- [ ] **D** Asking each person to flip a coin and selecting anyone who gets heads

☑ ☒ **Revise pages 115, 117**

65 Cumulative frequency

The cumulative frequency graph shows the weights of some eggs.

What was the median weight?

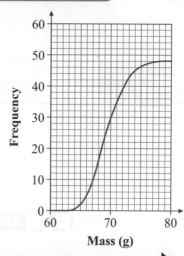

- [ ] **A** 70 grams
- [ ] **B** 69 grams
- [ ] **C** 72 grams
- [ ] **D** 24 grams

☑ ☒ **Revise page 118**

66 Box plots

This box plot shows the marks out of 30 for a group of students taking a spelling test.

Which of the following statements is **not** true?

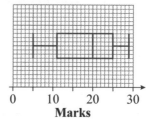

- [ ] **A** Half the students scored more than 20 marks
- [ ] **B** A quarter of students scored fewer than 25 marks
- [ ] **C** The lowest-scoring student scored 5 marks
- [ ] **D** The interquartile range was 14 marks

☑ ☒ **Revise page 119**

67 Histograms

Which of the following is **not** a true fact about histograms?

☐ **A** You can join the midpoints of the top of each bar to make a frequency polygon

☐ **B** The vertical axis is labelled 'frequency density'

☐ **C** You can have bars of different widths

☐ **D** The height of each bar represents the frequency for that class interval

☑ ☒ **Revise pages 120, 121**

68 Probability

The table shows the probability of each score on a biased dice.

Score	1	2	3	4	5	6
Probability	0.1	x	x	x	x	$2x$

Ravi rolls the dice. Work out the probability that it lands on 6.

☐ **A** 0.2   ☐ **B** 0.3

☐ **C** 0.36   ☐ **D** 1.2

☑ ☒ **Revise page 123**

69 Venn diagrams

A number is chosen at random from this Venn diagram.

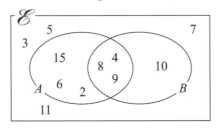

Work out the probability that it is a member of the set $A \cup B$.

☐ **A** $\frac{7}{11}$ ☐ **B** $\frac{3}{11}$

☐ **C** $\frac{3}{7}$ ☐ **D** $\frac{6}{11}$

☑ ☒ **Revise pages 125, 126**

70 Conditional probability

A bag contains 3 white counters and 2 black counters.

Two counters are chosen at random without replacement.

Work out the probability that the two counters are the same colour.

☐ **A** $\frac{9}{25}$ ☐ **B** $\frac{13}{25}$

☐ **C** $\frac{2}{5}$ ☐ **D** $\frac{3}{5}$

☑ ☒ **Revise pages 123, 124**

Answers to the Knowledge check are on the back cover (page 20) of this booklet.

My catch-up plan

Use this page to make your own customised catch-up plan. Write down all the pages that you plan to revise, then use the tick boxes to track your progress.

Page	Had a go	Nearly there	Nailed it!
......	☐	☐	☐
......	☐	☐	☐
......	☐	☐	☐
......	☐	☐	☐
......	☐	☐	☐
......	☐	☐	☐
......	☐	☐	☐
......	☐	☐	☐
......	☐	☐	☐
......	☐	☐	☐
......	☐	☐	☐
......	☐	☐	☐
......	☐	☐	☐
......	☐	☐	☐
......	☐	☐	☐
......	☐	☐	☐
......	☐	☐	☐
......	☐	☐	☐
......	☐	☐	☐
......	☐	☐	☐
......	☐	☐	☐
......	☐	☐	☐
......	☐	☐	☐
......	☐	☐	☐

Page	Had a go	Nearly there	Nailed it!
......	☐	☐	☐
......	☐	☐	☐
......	☐	☐	☐
......	☐	☐	☐
......	☐	☐	☐
......	☐	☐	☐
......	☐	☐	☐
......	☐	☐	☐
......	☐	☐	☐
......	☐	☐	☐
......	☐	☐	☐
......	☐	☐	☐
......	☐	☐	☐
......	☐	☐	☐
......	☐	☐	☐
......	☐	☐	☐
......	☐	☐	☐
......	☐	☐	☐
......	☐	☐	☐
......	☐	☐	☐
......	☐	☐	☐
......	☐	☐	☐
......	☐	☐	☐
......	☐	☐	☐

Notes

Use these pages to make any other catch-up notes you need. You could list topics that you know you need extra help with, or make a note of any facts or definitions you are struggling to remember. Or you could use them to record dates and times of catch-up sessions, extra tutorials or study periods.

Matching chart

You can use this chart to help you choose pages for your catch-up plan. Tick the units and topics you want to revise, and then add the pages listed to your plan on page 15.

Unit / topic	Revision Guide / Workbook pages	Revise? ✔
Unit 1: Number		☐
Calculations, checking and rounding	4, 6, 13	☐
Indices, roots, reciprocals and hierarchy of operations	2, 3, 4	☐
Factors, multiples and primes	1	☐
Standard form and surds	8, 12, 49	☐
Unit 2: Algebra		☐
Algebra: the basics	16, 17, 18, 21, 46	☐
Setting up, rearranging and solving equations	19, 20, 45	☐
Sequences	22, 23, 24	☐
Unit 3: Interpreting and representing data		☐
Averages and range	110, 111, 112	☐
Representing and interpreting data and scatter graphs	113, 114	☐
Unit 4: Fractions, ratio and proportion		☐
Fractions	5, 6, 9, 59	☐
Percentages	59, 62, 63	☐
Ratio and proportion	60, 61, 68	☐
Unit 5: Angles and trigonometry		☐
Polygons, angles and parallel lines	73, 74, 75	☐
Pythagoras' theorem and trigonometry	76, 77, 78, 79	☐
Unit 6: Graphs		☐
Graphs: the basics and real-life graphs	30, 55	☐
Linear graphs and coordinate geometry	25, 26, 27, 68	☐
Quadratic, cubic and other graphs	28, 29, 36	☐
Unit 7: Area and volume		☐
Perimeter, area and circles	80, 81, 83, 84, 104	☐
3D forms and volume, cylinders, cones and spheres	81, 82, 83, 85, 86, 87	☐
Accuracy and bounds	10, 11	☐

If your school follows the Pearson Edexcel two- or three-year scheme of work, you can use the shading on the left-hand side of the table to help you find the topics you are most likely to have missed between spring half term and the summer holiday. You can also check with your teacher to find out exactly which topics you should have covered during lockdown.

Unit / topic	Revision Guide / Workbook pages	Revise? ✔
Unit 8: Transformation and constructions		☐
Transformations	88, 89, 90	☐
Constructions, loci and bearings	91, 92, 93, 94, 95	☐
Unit 9: Equations and inequalities		☐
Solving quadratic and simultaneous equations	31, 32, 33, 34, 35	☐
Inequalities	37, 38, 41	☐
Unit 10: Probability		☐
Probability and counting	13, 123, 124	☐
Representing probabilities and outcomes	125, 126, 127, 128	☐
Unit 11: Growth and compound measures	64, 65, 66, 67	☐
Unit 12: Similarity and congruence	96, 97, 98	☐
Unit 13: More trigonometry		☐
Graphs of trigonometric functions	39, 49, 79	☐
Further trigonometry and solving 3D problems	99, 100, 101, 102, 103	☐
Unit 14: Further statistics		☐
Collecting data	115, 116, 117	☐
Cumulative frequency, box plots and histograms	118, 119, 120, 121, 122	☐
Unit 15: Equations and graphs		☐
Equations, inequalities and iteration	36, 38, 41, 45	☐
Using graphs	42, 43, 44	☐
Unit 16: Circle theorems	104, 105	☐
Unit 17: More algebra		☐
Surds, fractions and rearranging	46, 47, 48, 49	☐
Functions and proof	50, 51, 52	☐
Unit 18: Vectors and geometric proof	106, 107	☐
Unit 19: Proportion and graphs		☐
Transforming graphs and exponential graphs	40, 53, 64	☐
Gradient and area under graphs	54, 55, 56	☐
Direct and inverse proportion	68, 69, 70	☐

Two-year scheme of work units

Three-year scheme of work units

Knowledge check answers

1	C	2	B	3	C	4	A	5	C
6	B	7	A	8	D	9	A	10	D
11	B	12	C	13	C	14	D	15	B
16	B	17	A	18	B	19	C	20	A
21	B	22	C	23	D	24	B	25	D
26	D	27	A	28	B	29	A	30	A
31	A	32	B	33	D	34	D	35	C
36	C	37	B	38	A	39	A	40	D
41	C	42	B	43	C	44	A	45	B
46	D	47	C	48	D	49	B	50	C
51	B	52	D	53	C	54	C	55	A
56	D	57	C	58	A	59	B	60	D
61	C	62	C	63	D	64	A	65	B
66	B	67	D	68	B	69	A	70	C

Published by Pearson Education Limited,
80 Strand, London, WC2R 0RL.

www.pearsonschoolsandfecolleges.co.uk

Copies of official specifications for all Pearson qualifications
may be found on the website: qualifications.pearson.com

Text and illustrations © Pearson Education Ltd 2020
Produced, typeset and illustrated by
Florence Production Ltd, Stoodleigh, Devon UK

Cover illustration thumbnails by Pearson Education Ltd

The right of Harry Smith to be identified as author of
this work has been asserted by him in accordance with the
Copyright, Designs and Patents Act 1988.

First published 2020
23 22 21 20
10 9 8 7 6 5 4 3 2 1

British Library Cataloguing in Publication Data
A catalogue record for this book is available from the
British Library

ISBN 9781292374796

Printed in the UK by Ashford Colour Press

Notes from the publisher
1. While the publishers have made every attempt to ensure
that advice on the qualification and its assessment is accurate,
the official specification and associated assessment guidance
materials are the only authoritative source of information
and should always be referred to for definitive guidance.

Pearson examiners have not contributed to any sections in
this resource relevant to examination papers for which they
have responsibility.

2. Pearson has robust editorial processes, including answer
and fact checks, to ensure the accuracy of the content in
this publication, and every effort is made to ensure this
publication is free of errors. We are, however, only human,
and occasionally errors do occur. Pearson is not liable for
any misunderstandings that arise as a result of errors in this
publication, but it is our priority to ensure that the content
is accurate. If you spot an error, please do contact us at
resourcescorrections@pearson.com so we can make sure
it is corrected.

ISBN 978-1-292-37479-6

9 781292 374796 >